Piano Mix 1

Great arrangements for easy piano

Grades 1–2

Compiled and edited by David Blackwell

ABRSM

INTRODUCTION

The purpose of this collection is to bring a selection of pieces from a wide range of non-piano repertoire – orchestral, chamber, operatic, ballet, choral and vocal – into the hands of early-grade pianists. A variety of non-classical pieces, including spirituals, folk songs, TV themes, marches and jazz pieces, completes the span of music plundered, and the whole is offered to introduce players to the riches of music in all its forms and – it is hoped – provide quality repertoire that will engage and enthuse. If it also encourages players to seek out the original or explore new areas of music, then so much the better.

A number of considerations have guided the approach taken in this anthology. Firstly, we have looked for pieces that are characterful and tuneful. A vital consideration is that the arrangement is pianistic and fits comfortably under the hands. Much care also has been taken to ensure that the pieces suit the grade levels given: the label 'Grades 1–2' means that the pieces are mostly at Grade 1 level, with a few pieces also included as an introduction to Grade 2. Allowing for some flexibility, pieces are printed in approximate order of difficulty. In all this, a balance has had to be struck between playability and faithfulness to the original. It is not possible to render every detail of a complex original in a simple piano arrangement, yet the intention is that arrangements are respectful even if not always exact, and retain a sense of completeness.

The practice of arranging music and reworking it for different instruments has a long and distinguished history. In the Renaissance period, contemporary songs and airs were decorated in transcriptions for keyboard, for example in the *Fitzwilliam Virginal Book*, while Baroque composers regularly reworked both their own compositions and the work of others to make new pieces. The popularity of the piano in the 19th century as a domestic instrument saw countless transcriptions of orchestral and chamber pieces for piano solo or duet; in an age before recordings and mass concert-going, it was a means of discovering and appreciating a wide repertoire of music. Performance of different repertoire on the piano remains a satisfying musical experience, and we hope that these new arrangements will provide pleasure and delight for pianists of all ages.

David Blackwell

I should like to thank the many arrangers who contributed to this collection, ABRSM staff Rosie Cousins, Carolyn Fuller, Robert Sargant and Nigel Scaife, and piano moderator Tim Barratt for all their help. I also offer heartfelt thanks to adviser Jan Bullard, whose many technical and musical suggestions helped polish and refine the arrangements. *DB*

First published in 2015 by ABRSM (Publishing) Ltd, a wholly owned subsidiary of ABRSM, 24 Portland Place, London W1B 1LU, United Kingdom

Music origination by Julia Bovee
Cover by Vermillion
Printed in England by Halstan & Co. Ltd, Amersham, Bucks.

CONTENTS

Fireworks Minuet

from *Music for the Royal Fireworks*, HWV 351

Arranged by Alan Bullard

G. F. Handel
(1685–1759)

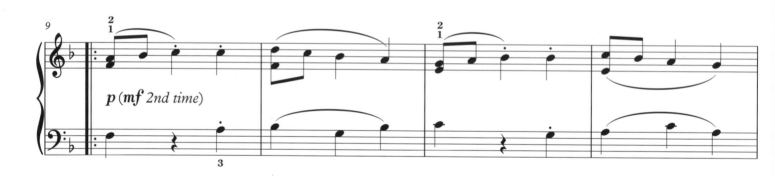

The composer George Frideric Handel was born in Germany but settled and lived in England, where he wrote operas, oratorios (large pieces for choir and orchestra based on a bible story) and much instrumental music. This is the second minuet from the *Music for the Royal Fireworks*, a suite for orchestra written in 1749 to accompany a vast fireworks display in London.

Did you know? Over 12,000 people attended a public rehearsal of this piece a few days before the first performance, causing a huge traffic jam!

Lullaby

No. 4 from Five Songs, Op. 49

Arranged by Nancy Litten

Johannes Brahms
(1833–97)

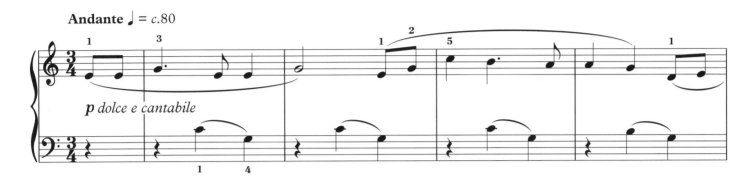

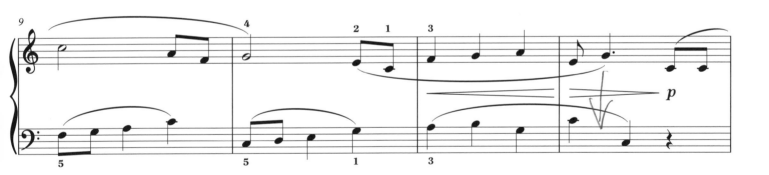

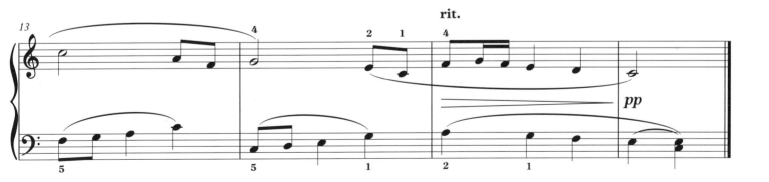

The German composer Johannes Brahms was one of the most famous composers of the 19th century, writing major works of all kinds for orchestra, singers and instrumentalists. This gentle lullaby is from a set of Five Songs, Op. 49, published in 1868, and was written for a friend of the composer's on the birth of her son.

Did you know? In the year the Lullaby was published, the world's first traffic lights were installed outside the British Houses of Parliament in London.

AB 3826

Strawberry Leaves

Arranged by Robert Pell

English Waits tune
16th/17th century

From the Middle Ages to the start of the 19th century, many British towns and cities had a band of musicians known as 'Waits'. Often playing pipes and reed instruments, their duties were to lead processions, welcome royal visitors at the town gates and wake citizens on dark mornings by playing in the streets.

Did you know? This lively tune is from the time of the Gunpowder Plot in England (1605), and may well have been played in the city of York where Guy Fawkes was born and grew up.

The Schoolmaster

from Symphony No. 55, Hob. I:55, second movement

Arranged by David Blackwell

Joseph Haydn
(1732–1809)

The Austrian composer Joseph Haydn wrote over 100 symphonies, many of them still performed today. This piece is from the slow movement of his Symphony No. 55, known from the early 19th century by the nickname The Schoolmaster, from the style and character of this movement. What kind of teacher do you think the schoolmaster was?

Did you know? A number of Haydn's symphonies have nicknames, including the Bear, Hen, Military, Clock and Drumroll. His Farewell Symphony ends with the musicians leaving the stage one by one until just two violinists are left!

Farmer's Song

Arranged by Alan Bullard

Traditional Slovakian

This Slovakian folk song tells of the life of a farmer. First he feeds the cows, then takes the sheep out to pasture, and so on. It's hard work, and all the time he is looking forward to when his son will take over the farm! The Slovakian title is 'Pridi ty šuhajko'.

Did you know? Slovakia or the Slovak Republic is a central European country that was one half of Czechoslovakia until the two countries split in 1993.

March

from *Rinaldo*, HWV 7

Arranged by Anne Marshall

G. F. Handel
(1685–1759)

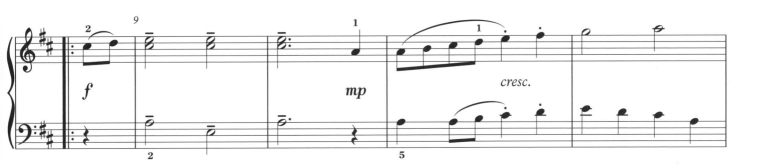

The composer George Frideric Handel wrote many famous works, including *Messiah*, the *Water Music* and the Coronation Anthem *Zadok the Priest*. This march is from his opera *Rinaldo*, set at the time of the First Crusade (11th century), when Western troops attempted to recapture the Holy Lands and Jerusalem. With magic and battle scenes, it proved to be Handel's most popular opera during his lifetime.

Did you know? In 1704 Handel was nearly killed in a duel with his friend, the composer Johann Mattheson – a large button saved his life!

Funeral March of a Marionette

Arranged by Christopher Norton

Charles Gounod
(1818–93)

Charles Gounod was a French composer whose most famous works were the opera *Faust* and *Ave Maria*, which adds a melody by Gounod to J. S. Bach's Prelude in C, from Part I of *The Well-Tempered Clavier*.

Did you know? A marionette is a puppet controlled from above by strings or wires. They have been popular throughout history, used in ancient Greek theatre, 18th-century opera (both Haydn and Gluck wrote theatre pieces for marionettes, and Mozart's operas have been staged with puppets) and in television and film: 'The Lonely Goatherd' sequence in *The Sound of Music* (1965) is a famous example.

Lute Song

from *The Firste Booke of Songes or Ayres* (1597)

Arranged by Nancy Litten

John Dowland
(1563–1626)

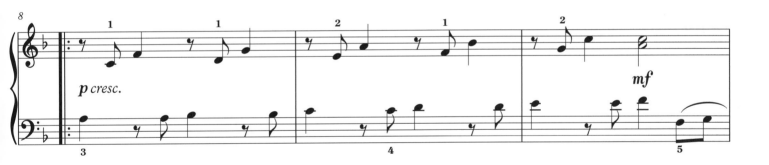

John Dowland was an English composer, lute player and singer, who worked at the royal courts in France, Denmark and England. This song was written for solo singer and lute (a plucked string instrument like a guitar but with a larger body, the shape of half a sliced pear) or for a combination of singers and instrumentalists.

Did you know? When he worked abroad, Dowland was accused of being a spy, plotting against Queen Elizabeth I.

In the Alps

Arranged by Alan Bullard

Traditional Swiss

(una corda)

This traditional Swiss tune is a 'ranz des vaches', a type of simple melody played on the horn by Swiss herdsmen as they called their cattle to be milked or drove them to pasture in the Alps. The mood is gentle, and suggests a calm pastoral scene.

Did you know? Ranz des vaches melodies are heard in a number of Classical compositions, including Beethoven's Pastoral Symphony, Rossini's overture *William Tell* and the *Symphonie fantastique* by Berlioz.

I want to be ready

Arranged by David Blackwell

Spiritual

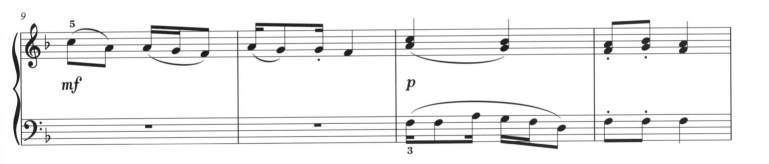

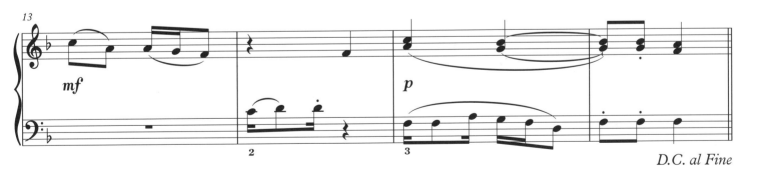

D.C. al Fine

The words of this spiritual are drawn from the book of Revelation, the last book of the Bible, and refer to the Christian's wish to live a good life and be ready to enter heaven.

Did you know? Spirituals are religious songs that were created and sung by African slaves in the southern states of America. The influence of African music can be seen in the use of syncopations (offbeat accents) and 'call and response', where one voice 'calls' part of the tune and another voice answers (e.g. bars 9–12 and 13–16 in this piece).

La donna è mobile

from *Rigoletto*

Arranged by Nancy Litten

Giuseppe Verdi
(1813–1901)

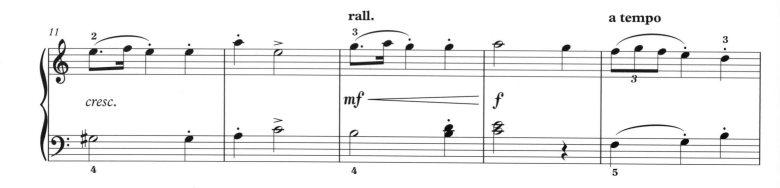

The Italian composer Giuseppe Verdi is regarded as one of the finest opera composers of all time, and his many operas are regularly performed around the world to this day. This famous tune is from his opera *Rigoletto* (1851), and is sung by the character the Duke of Mantua at the start of Act 3. The title means 'The woman is unfaithful', yet despite the Duke's observation it is the Duke himself who is not faithful to women.

Did you know? This aria shows off the tenor voice and was the highlight of the first performance. It is said that soon afterwards nearly every gondolier in Venice was singing it.

El noi de la mare

Arranged by Anne Marshall

Traditional Catalan

This simple tune originates from 16th-century Catalonia, a region in north-east Spain. The title means 'The Child of the Mother', referring to Jesus the Son of Mary, and in many countries it is sung as a Christmas carol.

Did you know? A popular folk custom in Catalonia is the building of human towers known as castells ('castles'). A solid crowd of people form the base, then more people climb on top to form up to eight or nine storeys with one person at the very top.

Fever

Arranged by David Blackwell

Dámaso Zabalza
(1835-94)

The Spanish composer Dámaso Zabalza was professor of piano at Madrid Conservatoire and also pianist to Queen Maria Cristina of Spain. This tango was originally a song (entitled 'Calenturas'), and the words tell of the poet's fever – a lovesickness that only his beloved can cure.

Did you know? The tango is a dance that began in Argentina in the mid-19th century. It mixed the regular phrases of European dances (brought by European immigrants to Argentina) with Cuban and Latin American syncopations to create a bewitching and popular dance form.

March of the Toreador

from *Carmen*

Arranged by Quintus Benziger

Georges Bizet
(1838–75)

Georges Bizet was a French composer and pianist, best known for the Symphony in C, composed when he was just 17, and for his operas. This song is from his most famous opera, *Carmen*, and describes the triumphant entry of the bullfighter or toreador Escamillo, who wins the heart of the attractive and alluring gypsy Carmen.

Did you know? Bullfighting is a traditional spectacle in Spain and Portugal that takes place in an open-air arena before a large crowd. The bullfighter, dressed in an elaborate, colourful costume, first challenges the bull, waving a large cape, then fights it with a sword. In recent times, protests have stopped many bullfighting events.

Sing, Cuckoo!

Arranged by Peter Gritton

Anon. English
mid-13th century

'Sing, Cuckoo!' is a round from medieval England that was sung to welcome the arrival of summer – the opening words in modern English are 'Summer is a-coming in, loudly sing, cuckoo!'

Did you know? A round is a piece of music in which the same melody is played or sung by all the parts but starting at different times, creating a piece in harmony. The melody of this piece (the top line of the right hand from bars 1–18) works as a round in four parts, each new part entering every two bars.

A Little Walk with Schubert

from Violin Sonatina in D, D. 384, second movement

Arranged by Kathy Blackwell

Franz Schubert
(1797-1828)

The Austrian composer Franz Schubert played the violin, viola and the piano, and was also a talented singer. He played the viola in his family string quartet with his brothers on violin and his father playing the cello. This tuneful piece is from the slow movement of his Sonatina in D for violin and piano.
Did you know? Although Schubert died at the young age of 31 he wrote a vast amount of music including symphonies, choral and chamber music, and over 600 songs. He once wrote eight songs in one day.

Trumpet Tune

from *King Arthur*, Z. 628

Arranged by Martin White

Henry Purcell
(1659-95)

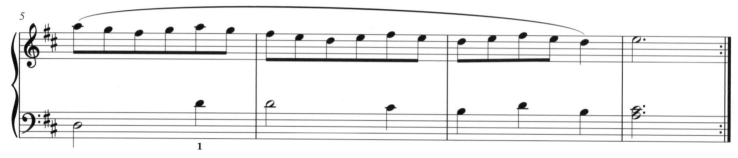

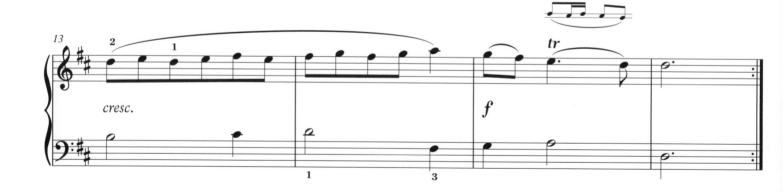

The English composer Henry Purcell served at the royal court in London as chorister, instrument-tuner, music copyist, organist and composer. This tune is taken from his dramatic work *King Arthur* (1691), which tells the story of the heroic British king.

Did you know? Although many characters and stories are connected with King Arthur - the wizard Merlin, the Knights of the Round Table, pulling the sword Excalibur from the stone - no one knows for certain if he actually existed.

A Duet with Mozart

No. 10 from 12 Duos, K. 487

Arranged by David Blackwell

W. A. Mozart
(1756–91)

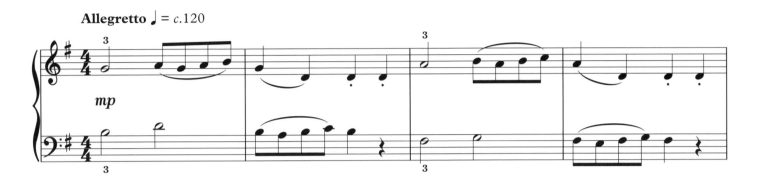

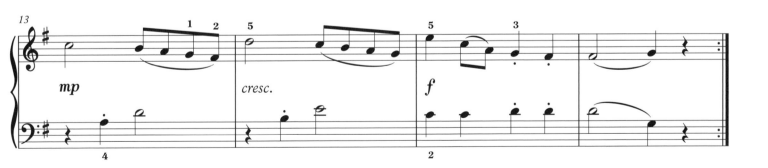

The Austrian composer Wolfgang Amadeus Mozart was one of the greatest composers of all time, writing over 600 pieces, from piano sonatas to symphonies and from operas to string quartets. This piece is from a set of 12 Duos for horn, written in 1786 and later arranged by Mozart for two violins.
Did you know? Mozart wrote his first keyboard pieces at the age of 5, his first symphony at 8 and his first opera aged 11.

Nocturne

from *A Midsummer Night's Dream*, Op. 61

Arranged by Peter Gritton

Felix Mendelssohn
(1809–47)

The German composer Felix Mendelssohn showed musical skill from an early age, giving his first public concert at the age of 9 and writing 12 string symphonies by the age of 14. This piece is from the music he wrote for a production of Shakespeare's *A Midsummer Night's Dream* in 1842; it is played between Acts 3 and 4 while the lovers sleep peacefully in the forest.

Did you know? Many other musical pieces have been inspired by Shakespeare's plays, including operas (*Macbeth*, *Otello* and *Falstaff* by Verdi), musicals (Bernstein's *West Side Story*) and orchestral pieces. The story line of the Disney hit film *The Lion King* (1994) is based on *Hamlet*.

Ja-Da

Arranged by Nikki Iles

Bob Carleton
(c.1894–1956)

Bob Carleton was an American jazz pianist who composed over 500 songs, including the hit song 'Ja-Da', written in 1918. The song became a jazz standard, performed by many artists and bands, including The Original New Orleans Jazz Band, Frank Sinatra and Oscar Peterson.

Did you know? 'Ja-Da' was used in the Tom and Jerry cartoon *Trap Happy* (1946), played as Butch the exterminator cat arrives to rid the house of Jerry the mouse – naturally, he fails!

The Music o' Spey

Arranged by David Blackwell

James Scott Skinner
(1843–1927)

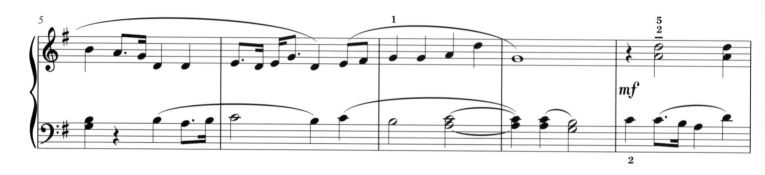

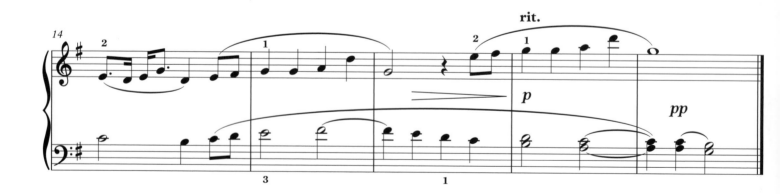

James Scott Skinner was a Scottish dancing master, violinist and composer and a key figure in Scottish traditional music. Famous as a virtuoso folk fiddler, he toured the UK and overseas and made a number of early recordings. This tune, named after the region in north-east Scotland, is one of around 700 that he composed, and was published in his collection *The Scottish Violinist* (1900).

Did you know? The semiquaver–dotted quaver rhythm (e.g. bar 2 right hand) is characteristic of Scottish folk music, and is known as a 'Scotch snap'.

St James Infirmary Blues

Arranged by Nikki Iles

Trad. arr. Joe Primrose (Irving Mills)
(1894–1985)

This blues piece is loosely based on an 18th-century English folk song called 'The Unfortunate Lad', which tells the tale of a young man whose immoral lifestyle led to illness and early death at St James Infirmary (or Hospital) in London. The tune with updated lyrics was popularized by Louis Armstrong and his Hot Five group in a famous 1928 recording.

Did you know? This simple tune has been covered by countless jazz bands and musicians, including Duke Ellington, Count Basie, Benny Goodman, Billie Holiday, and more recently by Diana Krall.

Royal March of the Lion

from *The Carnival of the Animals*

Arranged by Nancy Litten

Camille Saint-Saëns
(1835–1921)

Camille Saint-Saëns was a French composer, organist and pianist. This March is from his ever-popular *Carnival of the Animals*, a suite of 14 movements for two pianos and instruments portraying various animals from the elephant to the swan, and including 'Pianists' – strange creatures who practise scales all the time! In this piece, hold the pedal down in bars 9–11 and 13–15 for the lion's roar.

Did you know? The music from Saint-Saëns' Organ Symphony was used in the film *Babe*, based on Dick King-Smith's story of a sheep-pig.

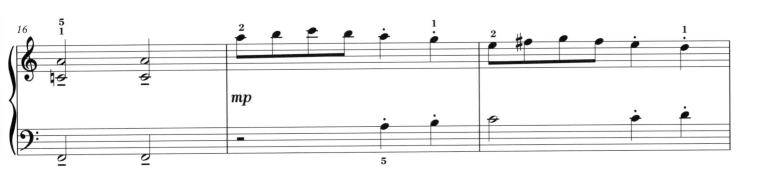

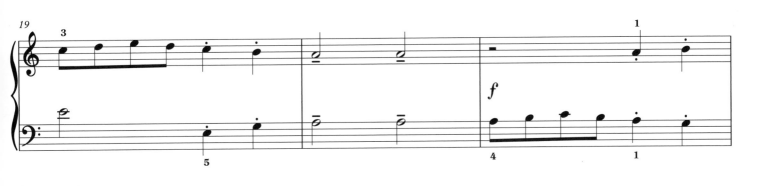

Bees-Wax Rag

Arranged by David Blackwell

Harry J. Lincoln
(1878–1937)

Harry J. Lincoln was an American composer of marches and rags who also ran his own publishing company, and wrote about both in his book *How to Write and Publish Music* (1926). This is an arrangement of the first section of one of his piano rags, published in 1911 at the height of ragtime's popularity. **Did you know?** The word 'ragtime' comes from the practice of playing simple, conventional melodies in syncopated, 'ragged time' to create a whole new style.